colour LOOKS

Si Salon Publishing Ltd

7 East Lodge, Inner Park Road, London SW19 6DE, England

Tel. +44 20 8785 2863 Fax +44 20 8785 0199

Devised & Produced by Simon Webb

Art Direction by Michael Breese

Reproduction and Print by Centro Grafico Ambrosiano, Milan, Italy

colourLOOKS

Front Cover Tina Paterson for Goldwell   Back Cover Zappas, England

Tina Paterson for Goldwell

Heading Out, Australia

Subway Service, Italy

Subway Service, Italy

Hammonds, England

Rob Harrelson Hairgroup
USA

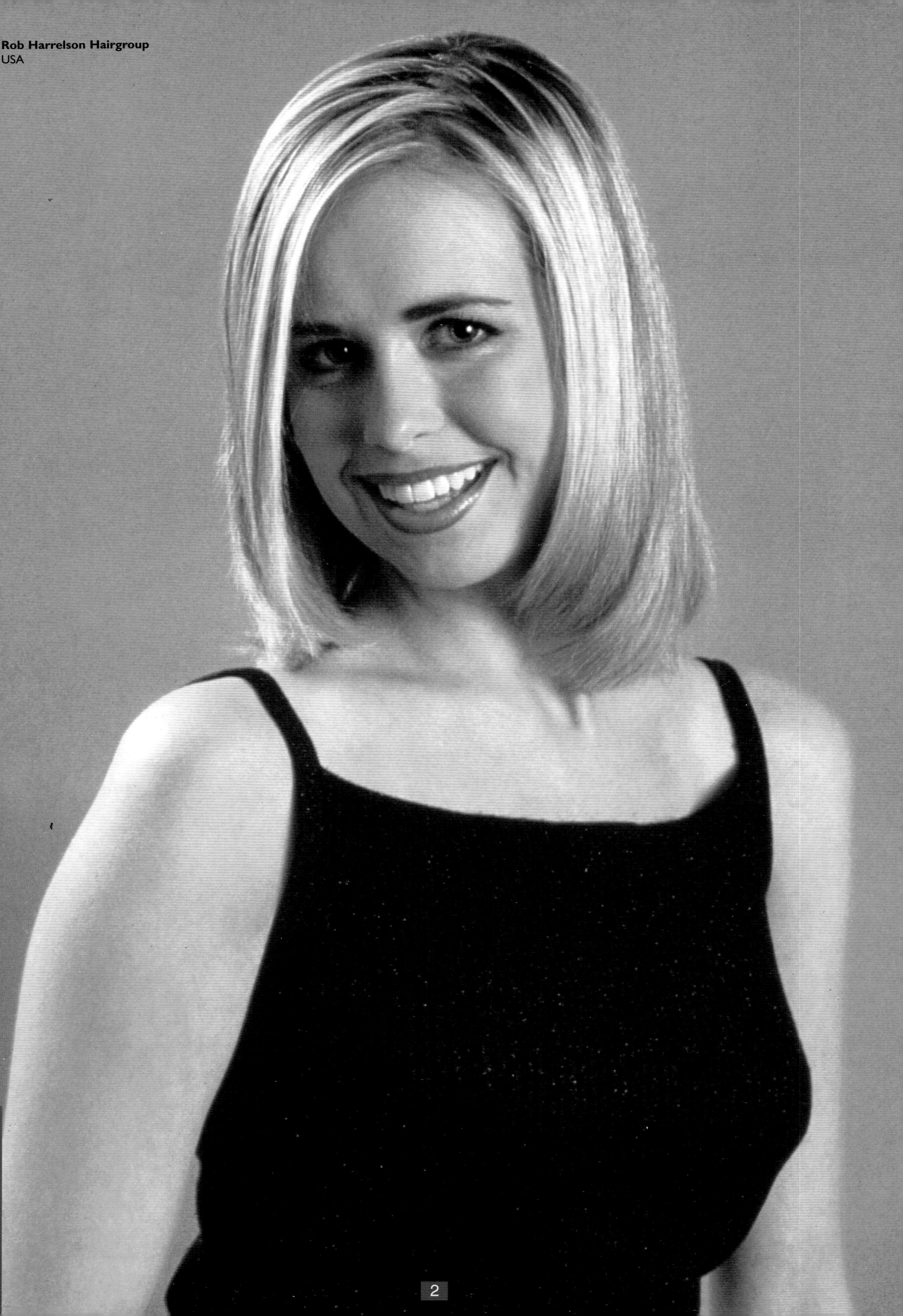

blondes

Tina & Simon Shaw
for Goldwell

Make Up Institute, Stockholm
Photography: Daniel Eriksson

Make Up Institute, Stockholm
Photography: Daniel Eriksson

blondes

Perry Anthony Design Group
USA

blondes

6

Noam Mazor for Indola
Israel

blondes

blondes

9

blondes

blondes

Brown's Art Team
for Goldwell Professional Haircare

blondes

13

Make Up Institute, Stockholm
Photography: Daniel Eriksson

blondes

14

GUILDFORD COLLEGE
of Further and Higher Education

blondes

Hair Port Salon & Day Spa
USA

blondes

blondes

18

blondes

Make Up Institute, Stockholm
Photography: Daniel Eriksson

blondes

20

Perry Anthony Design Group
USA

blondes

blondes

redheads

redheads

Make Up Institute, Stockholm
Photography: Daniel Eriksson

redheads

28

Make Up Institute, Stockholm
Photography: Daniel Eriksson

redheads

redheads

Bazzak Hair Design & Day Spa
USA

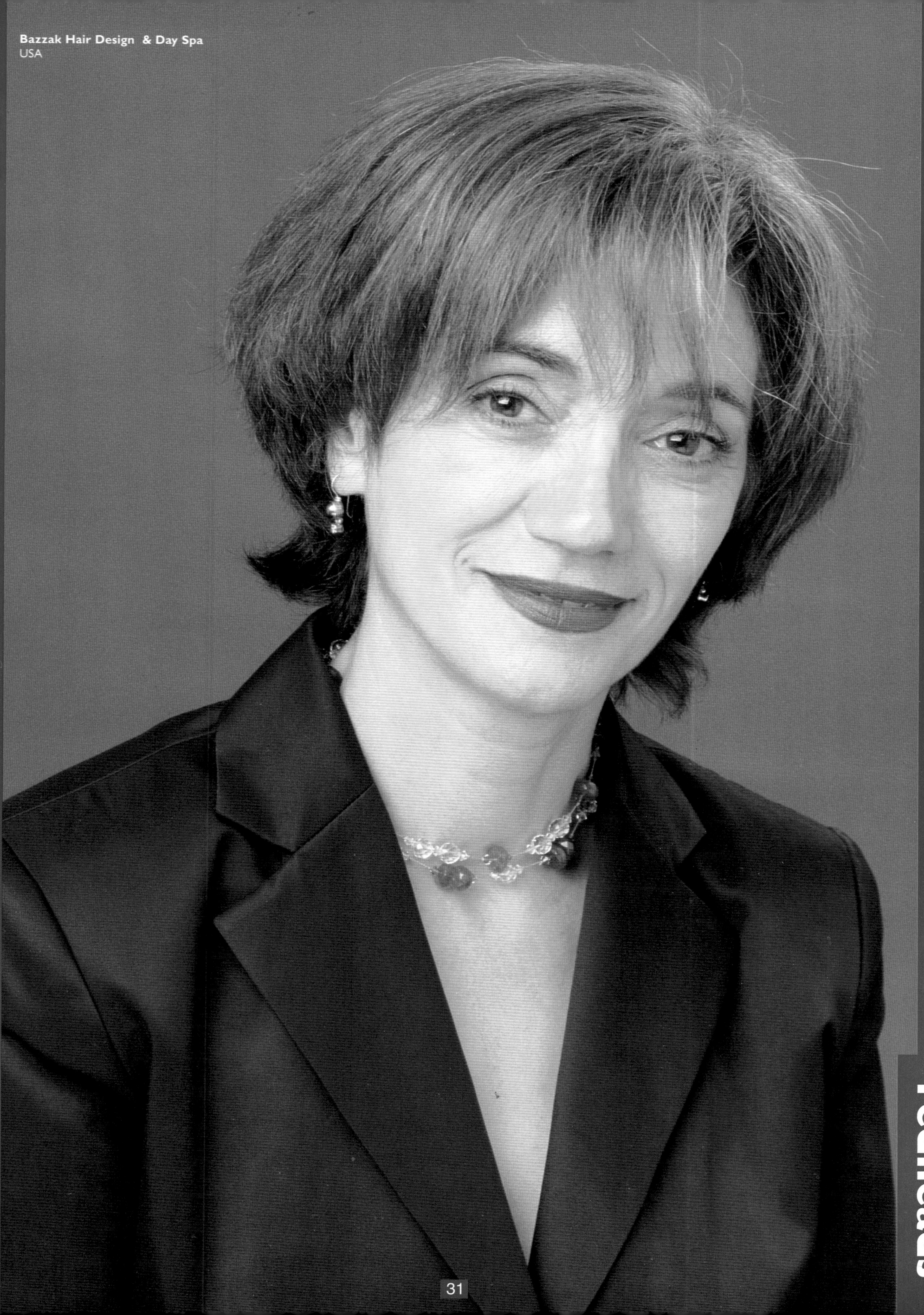

redheads

32

redheads

redheads

Errol Douglas
for Goldwell

Tina & Simon Shaw
for Goldwell

Make Up Institute, Stockholm
Photography: Daniel Eriksson

redheads

Errol Douglas
for Goldwell

38

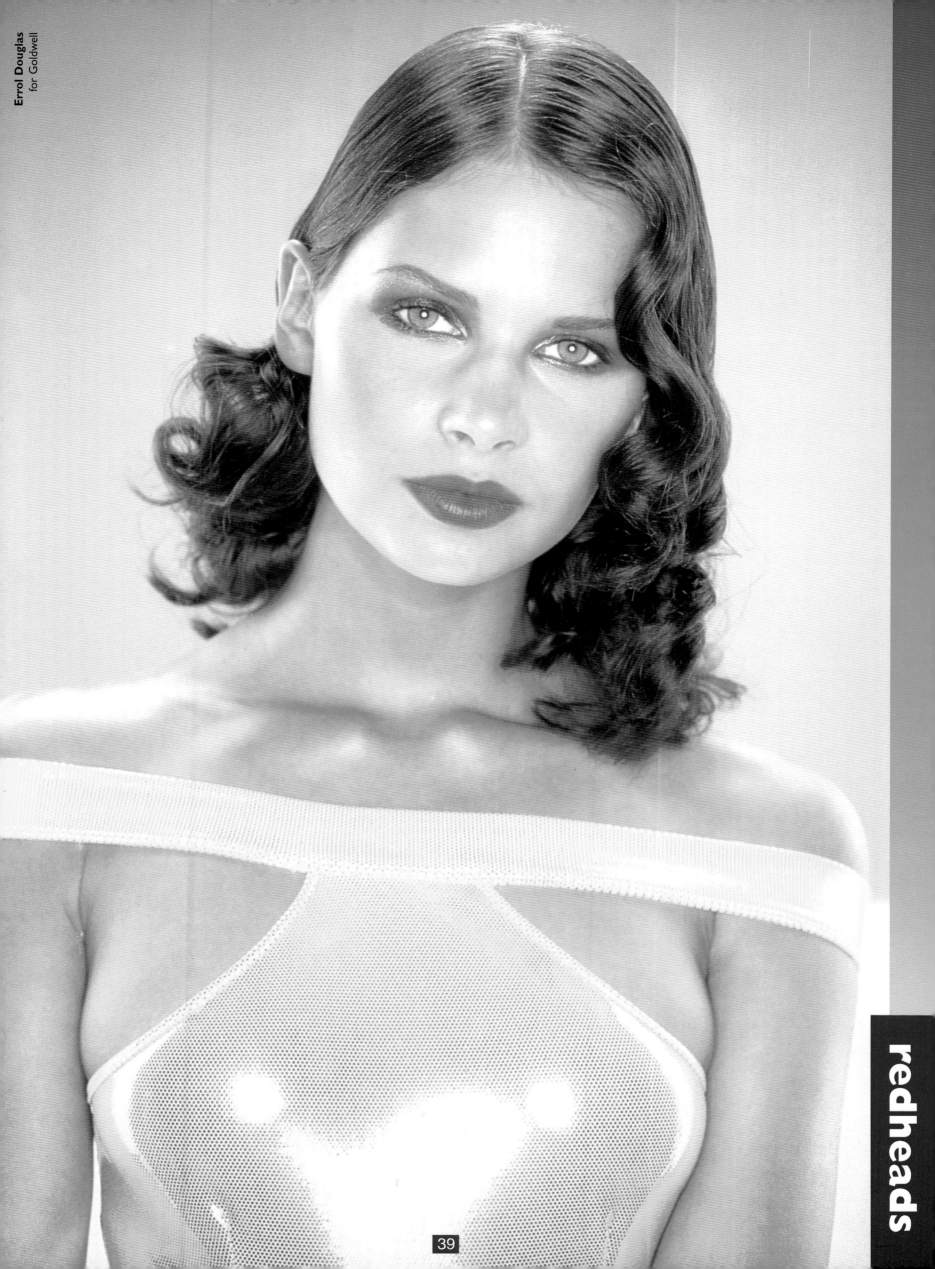

Errol Douglas
for Goldwell

39

redheads

Perry Anthony Design Group
USA

redheads

Currie Hair, Skin, Nails
USA

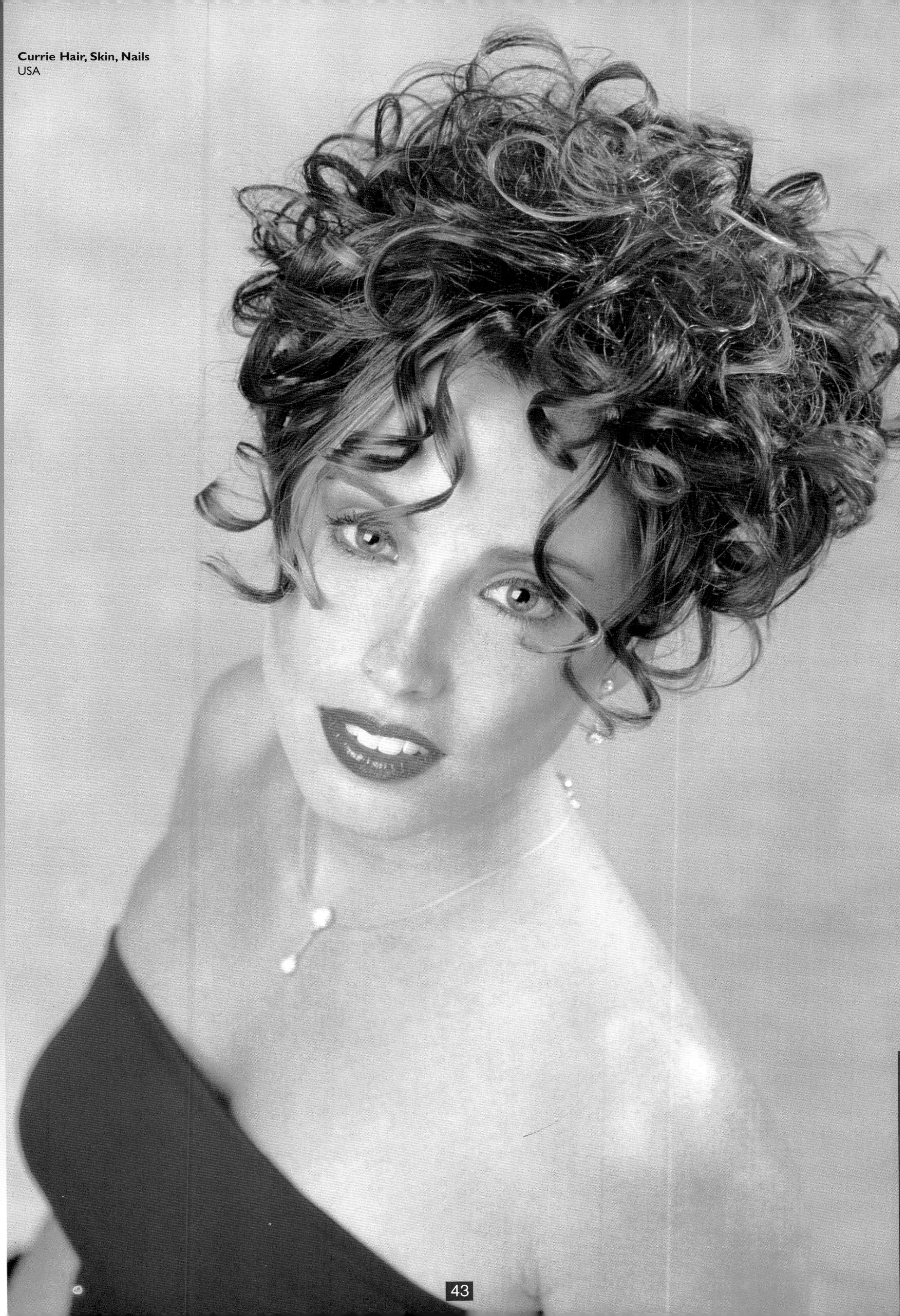

Make Up Institute, Stockholm
Photography: Daniel Eriksson

brunettes

44

Make Up Institute, Stockholm
Photography: Daniel Eriksson

brunettes

Tina & Simon Shaw
for Goldwell

Tina & Simon Shaw
for Goldwell

brunettes

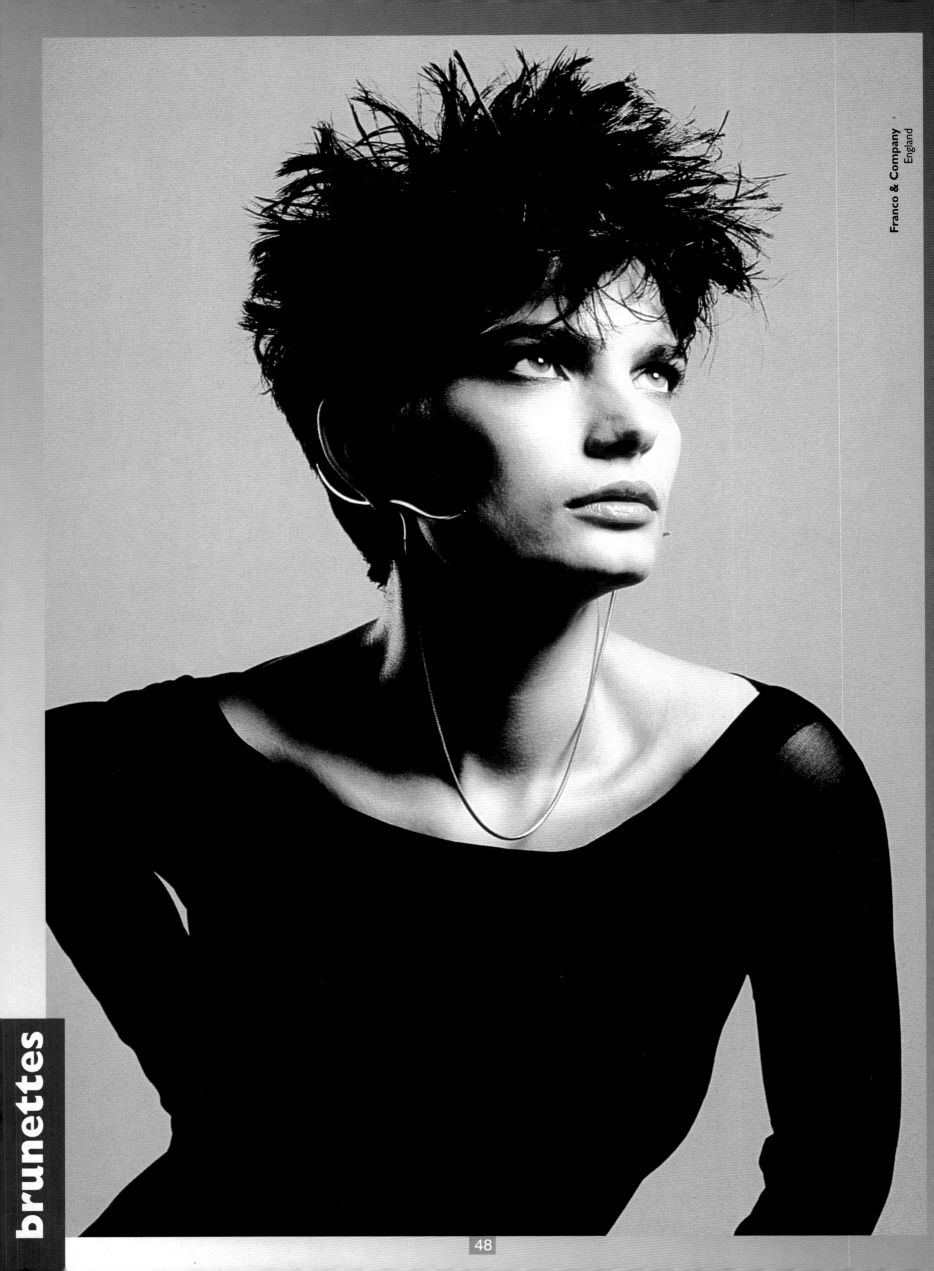

Franco & Company
England

48

Yosh Toya USA

brunettes

brunettes

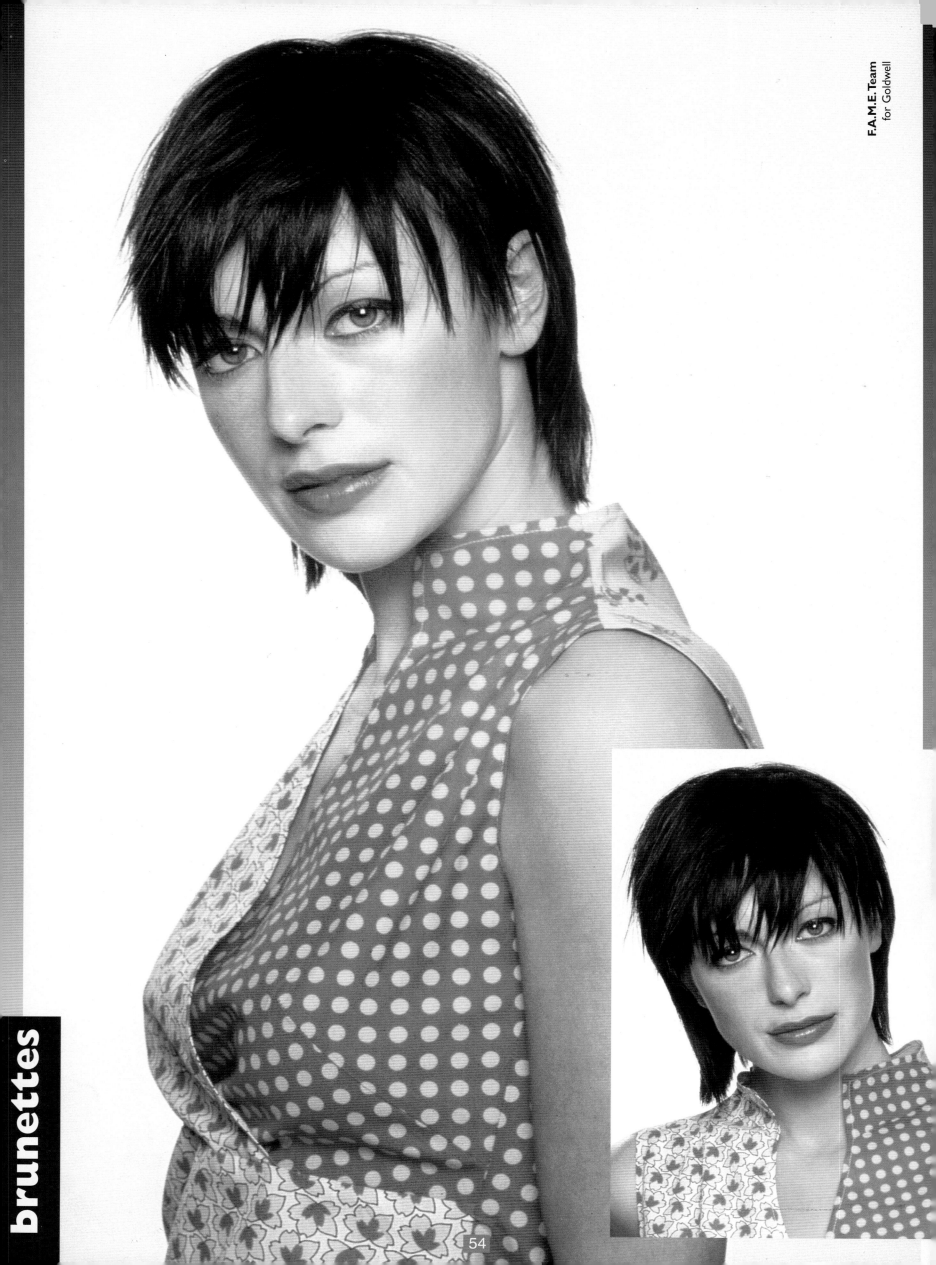

F.A.M.E. Team
for Goldwell

brunettes

54

F.A.M.E.Team
for Goldwell

brunettes

brunettes

brunettes

60

M & M Hair
for Goldwell

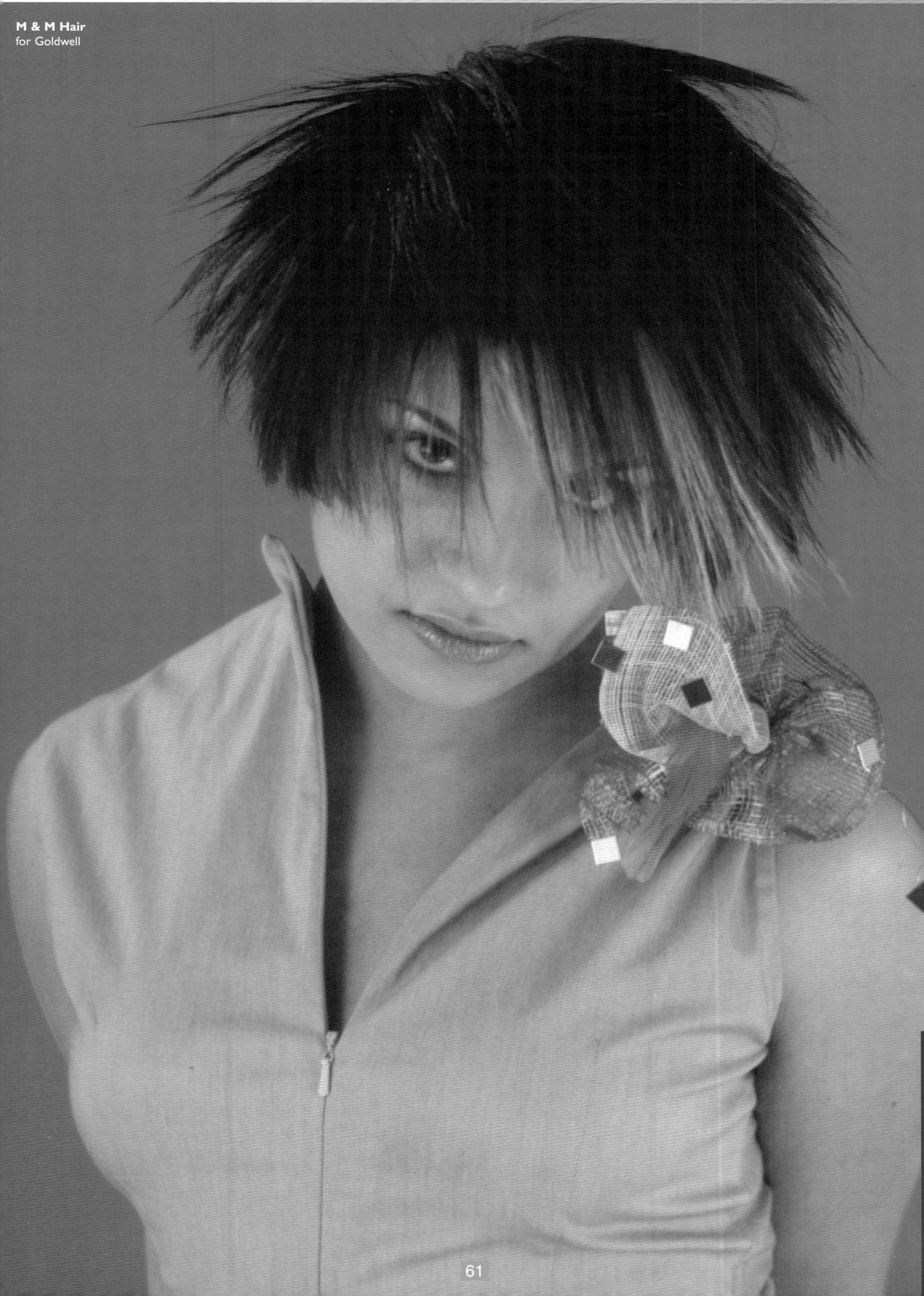

Perry Anthony Design Group
USA

brunettes

highlights

highlights

Make Up Institute, Stockholm
Photography: Daniel Eriksson

highlights

highlights

special fx

Noam Mazor for Indola
Israel

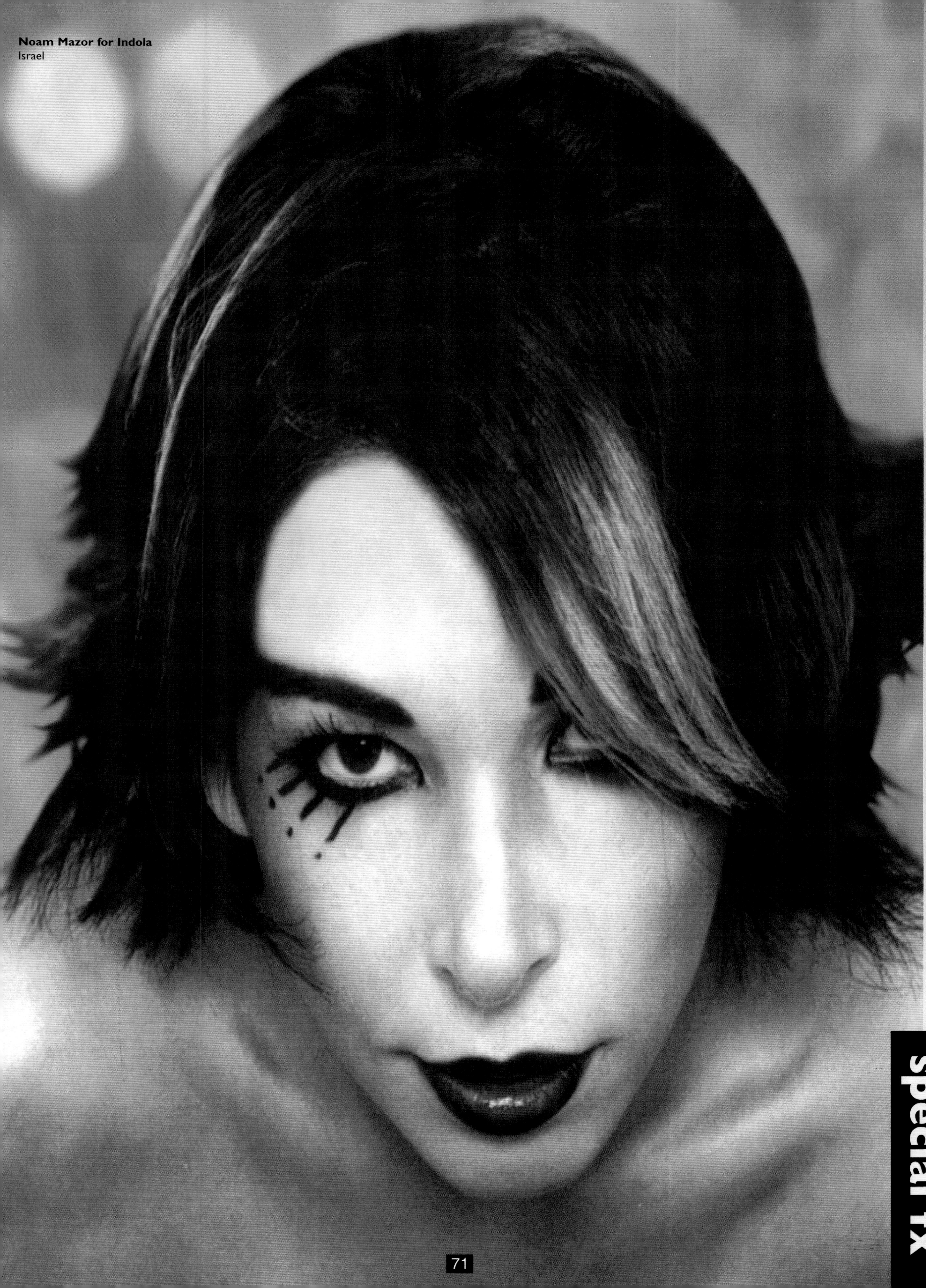

special fx

72

special fx

special fx

special fx

Shane Bennett
England

special fx

special fx

special fx

Make-UpArtist
EDUCATION

Film   TV   Theater   Commercials   Fashion

Stockholm´s Make-up Institute is widely recognised as the international school for the make-up profession. Hairdressers and students converge on Sweden´s capital to benefit from a full 16 week intensive education, whilst enjoying the rich and artistically inspiring culture Stockholm has become so famous for. Why not take the next step on a road to a glamorous and exciting future?

MAKE UP
INSTITUTE
STOCKHOLM

For more information please contact us on: Tel. +46 (0)8 30 06 40 Fax +46 (0)8 30 06 45

Make Up Institute Stocholm Freigatan 73 113 26 Stockholm Sweden www.makeupinstitute.com